Going Wild
Exploring the Marin Headlands

BONNY HINNERS

ILLUSTRATED BY **TOM BOLL**

Golden Gate National Parks Association

San Francisco, California

Library of Congress Catalog Card Number 98-73362

ISBN 1-883869-38-2

Designed and art directed by Jamison Spittler/Jamison Design, Nevada City, California

Printed on recycled paper in Hong Kong through Global Interprint, Inc., Santa Rosa, California

This book is dedicated to my exploring sons Bo and Davey, who share all their interesting finds . . . and to the resourceful people who work for the Golden Gate National Recreation Area and the California Academy of Sciences. They are the park rangers and librarians who help us learn what the interesting finds are and who make our explorations so much better informed. ~ BH

Mom wanted my sister and me to behave on a long shopping trip, but we were getting bored. That's when Mom promised we'd do something special the next day.

"David, Darla, if you two cooperate today, I promise you can go wild tomorrow," she said. She had something planned for us, but wouldn't tell us what it was.

That night, Mom looked at a map. She said she wanted to find the perfect place for us to go. Darla wanted to go to the zoo or the aquarium to see the animals, but I wanted to go to the beach.

"With any luck," Mom said, "we'll see animals before we get to the beach." Darla and I couldn't understand how that would work, but Mom said we should get up early for our surprise. I asked if she was planning a lot of running around, but she smiled and said, "Running? Not really."

We helped pack water and food for a picnic and snacks for the

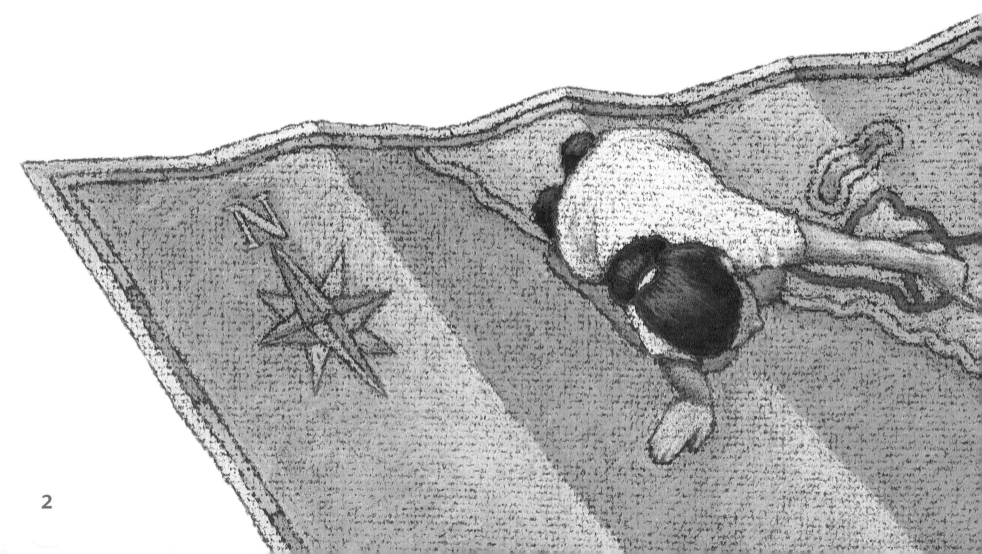

next day. We even packed chocolate bars. Darla wanted to eat hers right then. Mom said, "Pick out a short-sleeved shirt and a sweater to wear under your jacket. And David, please remind me to bring extra sunscreen."

Ranger Notes

- Always pack water to drink. Sugary drinks make you thirstier.

- Granola and cereal are carbohydrates and good for energy over a long time. Chocolate and even fruit have sugar and help give quick bursts of energy.

- Dressing in layers prepares you for any type of weather.

The next morning, I cheered when we went over the Golden Gate Bridge, thinking we were headed to the beach. Then we turned onto a different road than we usually take. Past the fruit stand and beyond all the houses, Mom parked far from the only building where the road ended.

"Where are we?" I whispered to Darla, ignoring the park sign. Mom stuffed her map into her backpack along with a pair of binoculars and a camera. Then she told us to tuck our pants into our socks to help keep ticks off. That looked pretty silly to me.

We started walking down a wide trail, but I thought it would be more fun to run. Darla tried to keep up with me and we couldn't stop laughing. Mom said we'd never see anything that way. She promised that if we walked quietly, we would see all kinds of wild animals and plants on our headlands hike.

"That's what I meant when I said we'd be going wild today," she said.

Ranger Notes

⌁ Strictly speaking, you can't bring anything home from national parks—no shells, rocks, flowers, twigs, or leaves—because each is an important part of the nature of the area, the ecosystem. Bring a camera so you can take home pictures instead.

⌁ Ticks don't know that you aren't supposed to take anything out of a national park. These tiny insects get on people and animals to suck their blood, and some carry Lyme disease. Always do a tick check after hiking. Ticks can be as small as a freckle.

Walking quietly didn't exactly sound like going wild to me. After a minute, I told Mom that I hadn't seen anything yet.

"Then you need to practice using your senses," Mom said. "Stand still and be quiet for a minute."

When we settled down she whispered, "Listen for animals moving or calling to one another." I heard a lot of birds singing and looked toward the sound. There they were. Two tiny birds flying around a clump of tall, scraggly looking bushes that Mom later told me were coyote bushes.

"Look for moving things and colors all around us." I noticed a flash of red on the shoulder of a black bird sitting nearby.

"Sometimes we can even touch or smell things." I took a deep breath. The tingling smell of eucalyptus trees made my nose itch a little.

Mom pointed out a plant with shiny leaves. "Look out for this one, it's poison oak. It'll give you a bad, itchy rash."

POISON
OAK

REDWING
BLACKBIRD

- Coyote bush gets its name from wisps of seeds in autumn that look like coyote fur caught in its branches.

- Some cough drops contain oil from eucalyptus trees.

- Shiny leaves in clusters of three on a stem may be poison oak. It looks similar to blackberry plants, which have prickly, fuzzy leaves.

When I said, "Don't forget our sense of taste,"
Darla wanted to have her chocolate bar right then.
By the side of the trail, I saw a funny yellow-orange
flower called sticky monkey flower. Mom told us this one was
safe to touch. The bottom side of its leaves was sticky like a piece
of tape. I picked a leaf to see if it would stay on my finger when I
held up my hand, and it did. But Mom said we shouldn't pick
things or expect to take anything home.

"We should leave the park the way we find it, David,
so we can enjoy it again another day," she said.
After walking quietly for a while, we came to

CALIFORNIA
QUAIL

STICKY MONKEY FLOWER

another path on our right. Just down that path was a round, gray-and-gold bird with a single curly feather on top of its head. The bird puttered around the trail and bushes without noticing us and finally slipped into a thicket of blackberry bushes. It was a California quail. Many animals, like quail, come out during cool morning and evening hours to look for food.

Ranger Notes

- ⚲ Sticky monkey flower gets its name from its sticky leaves and from its flowers, which some people think look like grinning monkey faces.

- ⚲ California quail, the state bird, usually travel in groups known as coveys.

- ⚲ Animals that are most active at dawn and dusk are referred to as "crepuscular."

"Let's follow that cute bird," Darla said. But Mom had told Dad we'd be going the other way. She said you should always tell someone where you plan to hike in case something happens and you need help. Also, according to our map, the path Darla had wanted to take didn't even lead to a beach, and I was excited about the beach.

A group of hikers crested a hill to our right, where the other trail would have taken us. Just then, something large ran downhill, away from them.

It was golden, like the grasses all around it. "Wow, did you see that? I think that was a mountain lion," I said.

Mom said it could have been a mountain lion, but was probably a deer. It would be unusual to see mountain lions. Since mountain lions eat deer, deer outnumber mountain lions in the balance of nature. Deer eat plants, which outnumber deer.

"Imagine a pyramid," she said, "with one mountain lion on top of a bunch of deer and even more plants at the bottom."

The only trees seemed to be eucalyptus, the ones with the bright, peppery smell. Mom said eucalyptus trees come from Australia, not America. Willows, oaks, and redwoods grow in northern California, but lots of these were cut down to supply building materials and firewood and to open up land for farming. When farmers wanted to reduce wind, they planted quick-growing eucalyptus trees.

ARROYO WILLOW

In the headlands, willows grow in riparian woodlands. Mom said these moist areas are special because they have a lot of different plants. Trees, shrubs, ferns, and wildflowers grow there, but not as much around eucalyptus trees. Because eucalyptus grows quickly and spreads easily, native trees and plants have trouble competing for sunlight, water, and soil.

"Shh, Mom, I hear an owl snoring," Darla said. I was about to laugh, but then I heard the coo-coo-coo sound that Darla must have heard.

Ranger Notes

⚐ "Riparian" means located near rivers, creeks, and streams.

⚐ Native plants and animals are those that have historically lived in an area. Non-native plants and animals are those that people have brought into an area.

COAST LIVE OAK ACORNS

BLUEGUM EUCALYPTUS TREES

"Oh, Darla, I think a dove is making that sound," Mom said. "But great horned owls do make homes in these big trees. If we look carefully, maybe we will see one sleeping there."

"Is that an owl?" Darla asked about a bird flying overhead. Mom looked through the binoculars and said she thought the bird was a red-tailed hawk. Two big black birds flew over the hillside just behind us. Maybe they were turkey vultures.

GREAT
HORNED
OWL

RED-TAILED
HAWK

Ranger Notes

⚘ Owls are nocturnal, most active at night. Hawks and vultures are diurnal, most active during the day.

⚘ As many as 21 different species, or types, of hawks have been seen in the San Francisco Bay Area in a single year.

We stopped for our snack, and Darla wanted to eat her chocolate bar right then, but Mom made her wait. Mom let Darla and me use her camera to take pictures of wildflowers around the rocky cliff. We looked some up in a wildflower book. Shooting stars, western hound's tongues, purple lupines, and orange poppies were blooming.

We saw butterflies too. I tried to take a picture of a blue one I liked, but it flew away too quickly.

"I wonder if it was a mission blue butterfly?" Mom said. "It's endangered, so park volunteers have been planting silver bush lupine to increase its habitat."

PIPEVINE
SWALLOWTAIL

16

We also saw orange monarchs and yellow tiger swallowtails.

We saw more birds and bugs as the trail got closer to the creek and the lagoon. White egrets stood at water's edge. From a bridge across the creek, we saw stiff lichens growing on trees all around. Water skimmers darted about on the surface of the water. Dragonflies and damselflies flew on practically invisible wings. Black pipevine swallowtail butterflies gathered in mud puddles.

DRAGONFLY

Ranger Notes

↝ Mission blue butterflies prefer to lay eggs in only three kinds of lupine, which their larvae, or caterpillars, will later eat.

↝ Endangered species are plants and animals of a particular type, like the mission blue butterfly, that may become extinct if not protected.

↝ A habitat is a place where a specific plant or animal makes its home. It offers food, shelter, water, space, and other living things, all of which the plant or animal needs to live.

↝ Dragonfly and damselfly larvae live in water, then climb out and shed their skin. After shedding, they have wings and are adults.

CALIFORNIA POPPY & PURPLE LUPINE

We didn't see any land animals here, but we could tell they had been here for a drink, or maybe to hunt for food, because we saw their tracks in the mud. Mom gave me a piece of paper and a pencil so I could draw pictures of tracks. Later, we'd find out what kind of animals might have been here. I copied some that were about three inches across. Oh man—I thought they'd be mountain lion tracks, they were so big. Another track had sharp claws on skinny fingers.

RACCOON

RABBIT

18

Darla and Mom pressed leaves onto an inkpad and then onto a sheet of paper. They only used leaves they found on the ground and they made sure none were poison oak. They washed the ink off their fingers, and rain would wash the leaves.

When we finally made it to the beach, we were all hungry again. After lunch, Mom packed all our trash to take back home. I thought that carrying trash in our backpack was weird. I mean, Dad always complains when he finds rocks in my pockets in the laundry. But Mom said there aren't always trashcans and our trash is bad for plants and animals. Plants don't grow well in trash. Animals may get sick or die if they get tangled up in our trash or even eat our food.

"Yuck!" Darla said kicking something in the sand, "Somebody left trash. Should we take that too?"

Large cliffs and hills surrounded the beach and the sand was dark. Mom told us about a shipwreck just off the coast. Only that ship didn't exactly crash. As he sailed through the fog, the captain saw that he was heading into cliffs, so he steered onto the sandy beach and everyone got off the ship. They even removed some of their cargo before the waves became too dangerous.

Ranger Notes

⤹ In 1853, the SS *Tennessee* ran ashore in Marin. The San Francisco Bay has been an important shipping route since 1849, but many ships missed the narrow entrance to the bay now spanned by the Golden Gate Bridge.

Mom said it was time to head back because she didn't want Darla to get so tired she wouldn't be able to walk back to the car. Darla said this was our longest walk ever, but Mom said we had walked even farther on our downtown shopping trip. I didn't want to go home yet, but Mom wouldn't let me stay, even though I promised to catch up to them later. She said that it's safest to stay together on a hike. We walked all that way and hardly stayed at the beach. It may be safe to stay together, but I lagged behind a little anyway.

When Mom and Darla stopped, I thought they were waiting for me, but they didn't turn or call for me to hurry up. They were looking at the ground. Just before I reached them, they turned and Darla said, "David, David, I just saw my first real snake!"

Mom said, "It was sunning itself in the path, but slithered into the underbrush to hide." I can't believe I missed it, a real snake. Darla said she couldn't wait to tell everyone in her class about seeing a real snake.

Snakes and other reptiles are cold-blooded. This means they can't regulate the temperature of their bodies like people and other mammals, which are warm-blooded. They lay in sunny areas to get warm.

On our walk back to the car, Mom told us about the Coast Miwok Indians from around here, and pointed out plants that they might eat. But some are poisonous, she said, and told us we should never eat wild plants.

California Indians long ago figured out uses for plants they knew were safe and even some plants they knew were poisonous. Safe plants were used not only for food, but also for medicine and as material in weaving, among other things.

Still, Darla kept talking about the snake she had seen. "Some people are scared of snakes, but not me," she said. "I just let it go right on by."

The walk back seemed really long and we stopped a lot and had more snacks. Darla finally got to eat her chocolate bar, but she didn't seem interested in it any more. She wouldn't stop talking about the snake.

"It was yellow with red stripes. And it was close; it was closer than that rock."

I was upset because I missed it. "It's not fair," I said, but Mom said we had all been lucky to see so many different animals and flowers. I was still disappointed about missing the snake though.

Ranger Notes

↵ Plants that the Miwok and other American Indians have used for food include miner's lettuce, oak, mariposa lily, yerba buena, toyon, manzanita, shooting stars, soap root, and wood hyacinth.

↵ Plants used for weaving include willow, tule, maidenhair fern, alders, sedges, rushes, and even poison oak.

I guess I was sulking because I stayed on the other side of the trail away from Mom and Darla. I didn't want to keep hearing about that snake. Suddenly, I heard something rustling in the dry brown twigs. Maybe it's another snake, I thought, and looked in the direction of the sound.

I saw a fat brown mouse. It crouched very still and watched me. We stared at each other, me and the mouse, for a minute, but when I moved just a little to see it better, it turned and ran. I don't know where it disappeared. It was even faster than the butterflies and harder to see because of its camouflage.

Darla talked about that snake all the way back to our car, but I didn't talk much about the mouse. I wanted to think about it and keep a picture of it in my mind. When we finally made it back to our car, we were really tired. Darla said she wanted a nap in the car, but Mom said we had one more stop first.

Camouflage helps animals blend in with their surroundings to avoid predators. Having the same color as plants and soil in your habitat is one way to be camouflaged. Having a shape that is similar to rocks or plants helps too.

"I don't want to go to the zoo anymore, Mom," said Darla. "Not after I got to see my snake."

We stopped at the National Park Service Visitor Center. The building had been an Army chapel before the area became a national park. Now it has exhibits about the park and things to do. Darla and I sat in a shelter like the Coast Miwok Indians built. After that, we saw a painting of an egret eating a goby. Mom read the sign by the painting and explained that the native tidewater goby, which birds like to eat, is endangered.

TIDE WATER GOBY

The painting showed cargo ships taking on water when they leave a port and dumping that water when they reach their destination. Animals in this dumped water may make homes in the new area. Yellow-fin gobies brought from European oceans are now taking over the tidewater goby's habitat. I remembered the eucalyptus trees and how they replaced native plants. Mom said that this reduces biodiversity. When one plant or animal replaces another, the balance of nature may be affected.

Ranger Notes

- National Parks are areas set aside by the government. Parks preserve and protect natural and cultural resources, including rare and endangered species as well as historic buildings and structures.

- In July 2000, the U.S. government listed 498 animals and 735 plants as threatened and endangered species. Over 275 of those are found in California.

- Biodiversity is a big word to describe the fact that there are many different plants and animals in the world. This diversity benefits people because we depend on an increasing variety of plants and animals.

A National Park Service ranger working at the visitor center asked about our hike. I showed her my drawings of animal tracks and she said one was a deer, one was a raccoon, one was a rabbit, and the other was a dog, not a mountain lion like I thought.

"Mountain lions and bobcats don't leave claw marks," she said. "They retract their claws to keep them sharp. Dogs can't." She also said we'd be among the luckiest people in the state if we saw a mountain lion, because they are rarely seen. "Some people report seeing mountain lions when they've really seen a bobcat, which is common in the headlands. If you do see a mountain lion, stay with your hiking buddies and try to scare it away," she said.

Of course, Darla told her about the snake she saw. The ranger said a lot of people were reporting seeing garter snakes, which aren't poisonous. I told her about the mouse I saw.

"That may have been a deer mouse or meadow vole. Did it have mouse ears or vole ears?" I remembered big mouse ears.

"That shows remarkable observational skills. They're usually nocturnal," she said.

After that, I felt even better about seeing it instead of the snake. "I might want to be a park ranger when I grow up," I told her.

"That's great. You're off to a good start by learning about nature," she said.

We stayed to talk with the ranger and look at the different exhibits in the visitor center. Oh yeah, there *are* things you can take home from national parks besides your trash and your pictures. The visitor center has brochures, books, maps, calendars of events, and other souvenirs. Darla was looking for a book about snakes when Mom told me she was sorry I didn't get to stay longer at the beach.

"That's okay," I said, "This place is pretty wild too."

Ranger Notes

⤳ Other names for the mountain lion are "panther," "puma," "cougar," and "catamount."

⤳ Bobcats are about half the size of mountain lions and have dark markings on their faces and bodies. They also have shorter "bobbed" tails.

⤳ Garter snakes have stripes ranging from brown to red and yellow running from head to tail.

Before we left, the ranger invited us to come back to do crafts or a hike with her or the other rangers and volunteers. We'll check the *ParkEvents* calendar and be back for sure.